About the Author

Dedicated to the education and well-being of children, Julie Anne Taylor wrote *Polka Dot Mask* to be a resource for families and educators. She is a professor in the Department of Education at the University of Michigan-Dearborn. Julie holds a doctoral degree from the University of Cambridge.

About the Illustrator

Ghassaq 'Gigi' Nassir specializes in watercolor paintings and sculpture. She is currently an honors student in the field of engineering and architecture at the University of Michigan. For a majority of her life, Gigi lived in Kuwait where she developed her love for art while attending the British School of Kuwait.

Polka Dot Mask

Julie Anne Taylor
Illustrations by Ghassaq 'Gigi' Nassir

Polka Dot Mask

Nightingale Books

A CIP catalogue record for this title is
available from the British Library.
ISBN 978-1-83875-392-4

Nightingale Books is an imprint of
Pegasus Elliot MacKenzie Publishers Ltd.
www.pegasuspublishers.com

First Published in 2021

Nightingale Books
Sheraton House Castle Park
Cambridge England

Printed & Bound in Great Britain

Dedication

To Leonard

Acknowledgements

We wish to thank the Office of Metropolitan Impact at the University of Michigan-Dearborn for its grant to support the creation of the watercolor paintings.

One mask
Two masks

Three masks
Four

What are we wearing these little masks for?

For Mamma,
For Papa,

For you

and for me

Wearing a mask is important,
you see!

White mask
Blue mask

Green mask
Red

Do we wear a mask in bed?

No, only where the virus could spread.

In public spaces,

we wear masks on our faces.

Striped mask
Plaid mask

Polka dot
Plain

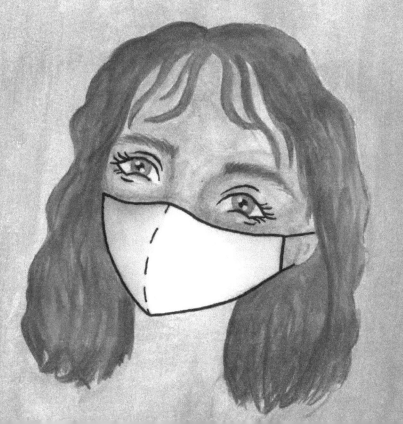

We don't have to look the same!

Over the mouth
And over the nose
That is where a mask goes!

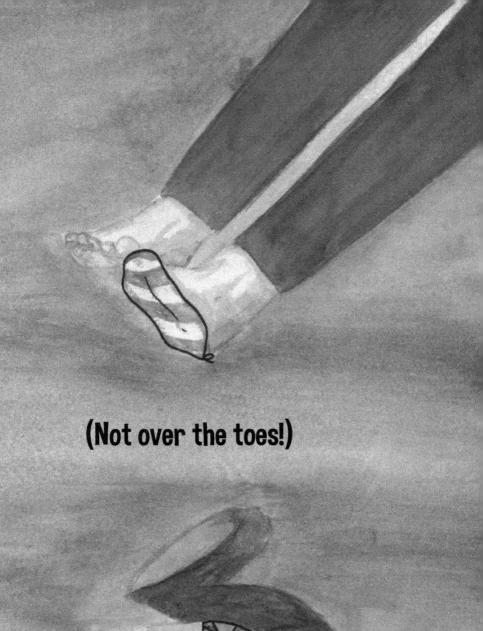

(Not over the toes!)

In rainy,

In sunny,

In cold

or hot weather.

Until all is better

We'll wear masks together.

CPSIA information can be obtained
at www.ICGtesting.com
Printed in the USA
BVHW020857251121
622335BV00019B/311